Contents

In This Issue

Letters to the Editor **2**
Letters

My Serve **4**
Poem

Play Volleyball! **6**
Article

He Kicks, He Scores! **14**
Story

Falling for Lacrosse **22**
Play

Features

Strategy Spot   Making Connections to Your Own Experiences _ _ _   5

Graphic Organizer   Comparison Chart _ _ _ _ _ _ _ _ _ _ _ _ _ _ _ 30

Project Ideas   Do a Radio Commercial/Experiment with Throwing _ 32

Glossary   _ 33

Letters to the Editor

Note from the Editor:
At POWER Magazine, we always like to hear from our readers.
We asked kids to write about their favourite sports. Here are
some letters from around the world.

Dear POWER Magazine,
In Trinidad and Tobago, we play cricket, field hockey, soccer, and volleyball. For cricket, you use a bat and a ball, so it's sort of like baseball. I love cricket, and I'm a better batsman than all my friends!
Anthony

San Fernando,
Trinidad and Tobago

Dear POWER Magazine,
You asked about favourite sports. Mine is table tennis. I like the game because it's fast. My cousins like basketball and soccer better, so I play those games a lot as well— and they play table tennis, too. Do kids in Canada play table tennis, basketball, and soccer?
Wang

Nanjing, China

Pelé

Dear POWER Magazine,
Soccer is the BEST! My sports hero is Pelé, who helped Brazil win three World Cup soccer championships. People here love soccer so much that we fill the 200 000 seats in the Maracana—the world's largest soccer stadium. When we are at the beach, we play my other favourite sport—volleyball.
Fernando

Rio de Janeiro, Brazil

Dear POWER Magazine,
Soccer and tennis are my favourite sports. I play soccer with my friends, and I play tennis with my family. When there's an important soccer game on television, everybody watches and cheers for their team.
Talia

Tel Aviv, Israel

Dear POWER Magazine,
I like basketball the best. I play it at the "halkevi"—the community centre. I swim and play volleyball there, too, but basketball is my favourite sport. I think a Canadian invented basketball. Is that true?
Anwar

Ankara, Turkey

My Serve

Poem by
Monica Kulling

I serve a slam ball
over
over the net!

      sneakers squeak
      bodies bump
      hands high
      every player
      ready
      ready!
      to volley
      to spike
      to slam back

my serve

Making Connections to Your own Experiences

Hi, my name is Striker.
I play soccer, but I like lots of sports.
Team sports are my favourites. What
sports do you like? What do you
know about the topic of sports?

Thinking about what you already know
before you start to read is called making
connections to your own experiences.

Making Connections to Your Own Experiences

Before you start reading the article "Play Volleyball!" on page 6,
think about your own experiences with sports. For example, think
about the following questions:

- Have you ever played on a team?
- What kinds of sports do you like playing?
- What sports do you watch on TV?
- What do you know about volleyball?

Connecting what you're reading with your own experiences can help you
as you read. Connections can come from things you've done, people you've
talked to, shows you've watched, or books and magazines you've read.

Play Volleyball!

Article by Philip Moore

Playing beach volleyball in Vancouver

On sunny beaches around the world, young people string up nets, slather on sunscreen, and bounce a ball back and forth. But what happens in Canada when the cold winds blow and the snow flies? Take the game indoors! That's the beauty of volleyball.

In 1891, Canadian Dr. James Naismith invented basketball while working in the United States. Four years later, William Morgan invented volleyball. Morgan decided that there needed to be a good alternative to basketball. He wanted a sport that could be played indoors but was easier for older people than basketball.

Today, more than 1 billion people—mainly young people—around the world play volleyball.

Volleyball has come a long way since it was invented in 1895. Now there are two kinds of volleyball—indoor volleyball and beach volleyball. The games have similar rules, but indoor volleyball is played on a court in a gymnasium and beach volleyball is played outdoors on sand or grass.

Both indoor and beach volleyball are Olympic sports. Beach volleyball became an Olympic sport in 1996.

Volleyball is a competitive sport, played by many fit, young athletes.

The Volleyball World Championships are held every four years in a different country.

Volleyball Basics

Volleyball is a team sport in which the players hit a round leather ball back and forth over a high net. Catching, throwing, and kicking the ball are not allowed. The basic moves in a volleyball game are serving, setting, spiking, blocking, and passing.

Often players jump in the air when serving the ball. This helps them hit the ball harder.

Each team wants the ball to hit the ground on the opponent's side of the net. Players try to make low, powerful shots that are hard for the other team to return. They try to block shots to their own side. When the ball is on their side, players do everything they can to keep the ball off the ground.

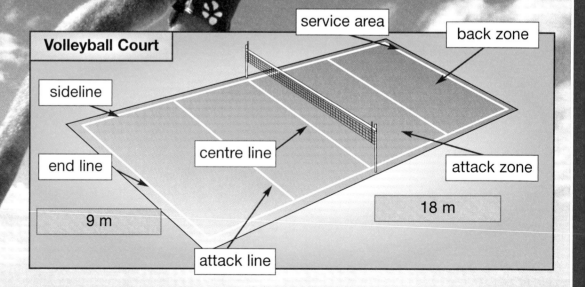

Volleyball Court

service area

back zone

sideline

centre line

end line

attack zone

18 m

9 m

attack line

Volleyball is played on a rectangular court with a net in the middle. Teams must stay on their own side of the net. Players are not allowed to touch the net when they hit the ball.

Indoor volleyball and beach volleyball have the net at the same height, and they use the same ball. However, the ball is not blown up as much for beach volleyball.

Another difference is that the court for indoor volleyball is bigger than the court for beach volleyball. Teams for beach volleyball usually have two players. Teams for indoor volleyball can have six players on the court at a time, plus extra players as substitutes.

These beach volleyball players are receiving the serve.

The Game—Play by Play

The game starts when one player serves the ball from the service area over the net to the opposing team. The server hits the ball **underhand** or **overhand**, using the **heel of the hand**. Team members take turns serving the ball.

The player leaping into the air hits the ball with one hand. This shot is called a spike. The spiker tries to make the ball hit the ground on the opponent's side.

After the ball has been served over the net, the receiving team tries to stop it from hitting the ground. A team can hit the ball up to three times on its own side before sending the ball back over the net.

The usual pattern is
- *bump*
  (slow down the ball and pass it to the next player)

  ↓
- *set*
  (send the ball high in the air to a spiker)

  ↓
- *spike*
  (slam the ball down onto the other team's side)

When the ball is close to the ground, a player might bump it. The player uses both forearms to bump the ball, keeping it from hitting the ground.

Each team tries to block the other team's shot.

Indoor Volleyball—How to Score

In indoor volleyball, only the team serving the ball can score points. The team scores a point …

- if the ball hits the floor on the other team's side of the net
- if the other team hits the ball more than three times before hitting it back over the net
- if the other team hits the ball into the net

The same player keeps serving until the team loses the serve. The serving team loses the serve if they hit the ball out of bounds or if the ball hits the floor on their side. The serving team also loses the serve if they hit the ball into the net.

When a team loses the serve, the other team has a chance to serve and score points.

Each game lasts until one team scores 15 points. A team must win by at least two points. The teams play either three or five games to see who wins the **match**.

The winning team members from Brazil congratulate each other after a match.

Beach Volleyball—How to Score

Many of the rules for indoor volleyball are also used for beach volleyball. But, in beach volleyball …

- a team can score points while serving or receiving
- the serving team does not lose the serve if the serve hits the net

In beach volleyball, a team must win a game by at least two points. The number of points that need to be scored can change for each **tournament**.

Teams can play just one game to see who wins the tournament, or they can keep playing until one team wins by two games.

Volleyball is a great game for players and spectators.

He Kicks, He Scores!

Story by Brian Roberts • Illustrations by John Mardon

The Storms had just won their semifinal game. Now they were going to the Manitoba soccer finals. Out of 64 teams in the league, only 2 were left to play for the championship—the Storms and the Blizzards. The big game was only one day away. The Storms were wild with excitement.

To the Storms of Winnipeg, the Blizzards were old rivals. The Blizzards had played skillfully during the season, but a lot of the players hadn't played fairly. They were ready to do just about anything to score points, and the referee didn't see every foul. Winning the championship was important to the Storms. Beating the Blizzards was even more important.

The Storms were a very good team. But one of their players, called Striker, was especially good. He was very fast—faster than any other player on the team—and he had the best shooting skills. Striker got his nickname because he was the highest-scoring forward on the team.

In fact, Striker was the best forward his coach had ever worked with. He could pass in any direction with either foot, dribble his way through a pack of defenders, head the ball, and shoot hard to the net. With Striker on the team, the Storms were sure of victory.

There was only one problem—Striker wasn't much of a team player. He knew that he was the star player, and he did things his own way. He was often late for practices and games, and the coach called him on it many times.

With Striker on the Storms' team, the Blizzards knew there was no way they could win the championship. So the night before the big game, some of the Blizzard players had a meeting. They were determined not to let one guy stop them from winning the championship.

Soon they came up with a plan. They decided that they had to keep Striker away from the stadium until the game was over.

Larry, a winger for the Blizzards, would put the plan into action. Late in the evening, Larry phoned Striker's house. Striker's older brother answered the phone. Larry pretended that he was one of Striker's teammates.

"Every day this week, Striker felt dizzy after training," said Larry, sounding very concerned. "Yesterday he fainted, but he wouldn't let me tell the coach. I just thought someone should know."

The next morning, Striker was busy packing his equipment. He was hoping that his dad could come to the game to cheer him on. His dad travelled a lot, but still came to Striker's soccer games whenever he could.

Just at that moment, his father came rushing into the room.

"Striker, how are you feeling?" asked Dad.

"Great, Dad. Ready for the game," said Striker.

"Are you sure?" asked his father. "You look worn out. Did you have breakfast this morning?"

"Well, no," said Striker. "It's the big game today, so I'm too nervous to eat. But I'm fine."

"You look very pale. And your brother tells me you were dizzy and you fainted. We're going to take you to the doctor. I'll phone your coach on the way to let him know where you are."

"But Dad...!" Striker shouted. "You can't. I have to play this game. The team can't do anything without me."

Striker protested, but it was no use. Striker's father and brother each took one of Striker's arms and walked him out to the van. Striker felt powerless as his older brother joked, "Don't try to get away."

In the back of the van, Striker slumped over, staring angrily at his father and brother. The game was about to start, and he wasn't there!

The Storms had gathered at the stadium. No one had seen or heard from Striker. That wasn't unusual, because Striker liked to be alone before a game. But when it came time to warm up and Striker hadn't come, they started to worry. Striker might be late, but he was never this late.

Coach told them not to worry, even though he was upset, too. He sent them onto the field to go through their warm-up drills. After a few stretches and some jogging, the Storms returned to the locker room. There was still no sign of Striker.

"Where is he?" asked Jason. He was the slowest player on the team, and the most willing to admit that he needed help. "We're doomed without Striker!"

Meanwhile, Striker, his dad, and his brother were caught in a traffic jam. Striker's father tried to call the coach on his cell phone several times, but there was no answer. He looked back at Striker and tried to cheer him up. Then he turned on the radio. The soccer game was being broadcast live. From his seat, Striker could hear every word.

The Storms had fallen behind the Blizzards 2–1 in the first half. Now it was well into the second half. The Storms were fighting back strongly. But they would have to score two goals in the next ten minutes to win the game.

Striker just had to escape. As the van waited at a traffic light and his father and brother listened to the radio, Striker unbuckled his seatbelt as quietly as he could. Then he opened the van door and jumped out. As he ran, he called, "I'm *not* sick. See you at the game!" His father shouted after him, but he knew that Striker was too fast for him to catch up.

19

Striker ran to the stadium. He realized how much the Storms meant to him. He couldn't let the team down!

When he reached the stadium, Striker looked at the scoreboard. The game was now tied 2–2 with only five minutes to go. Striker hurried into the locker room and changed into his uniform as fast as he could. By the time he ran out onto the field, two more minutes had ticked by.

The Storms were thrilled to see him, but the Blizzards couldn't believe their eyes. Seeing that the plan had failed, Larry angrily kicked Jason's leg and got a foul. The Storms were awarded a penalty kick. Time for Striker to move in! He kicked the ball right over the goalie's head and into the back of the Blizzards' net.

The game was over. The Storms had won, 3–2! The Blizzards watched them celebrating their victory. Then the Blizzards miserably left the field.

Now came the questions for Striker. "Where have you been?" the Storms asked. "We needed you! How could you miss most of the *final* game?"

"I'm sorry," said Striker. "My dad and my brother thought I was sick. They sort of kidnapped me to take me to the doctor."

"We knew that you wouldn't just forget about the game," said their coach. "But are you okay? What happened?"

Just then, Striker's father and brother appeared. They explained about the phone call the night before. Coach asked everyone on the team if they'd made the call, and all the players shook their heads.

"It must have been the Blizzards. We all know they would do almost anything to win," Striker said.

Jason couldn't stop grinning. "What the Blizzards did stinks. But you're okay, Striker, and *we won!*"

"Yup," said Coach, "knowing that everybody is okay is just as important to us as winning. But those Blizzards—they could be disqualified for a whole season! After all, soccer is all about teamwork and sportsmanship."

"That's a lesson I learned while I was stuck in the van," said Striker, looking at Jason and his other teammates.

"And I promise you I will never make Striker late again—traffic jams or no traffic jams," said Striker's dad. "After all, soccer is the greatest."

Falling for Lacrosse

Play by Claire Fontaine

Lacrosse is a fast-paced sport.

Characters

Mr. Bailey   René   Monique   Matt   Sylvie   Marcel

Scene 1—Room 101, a school in Montreal

Mr. Bailey

I have a surprise for you, class. We're going to learn about a new sport. I'll give you two clues, and let's see if you can guess what it is.

René

I know! It's badminton.

Mr. Bailey

Not so fast, René. Wait for the clues. First: it's a team sport. Second: there's a ball, but you can't touch it with your hands.

Monique

Is it field hockey?

Mr. Bailey

Good guess! But no. Here's a third clue: the game started in North America long before the Europeans arrived here. Matt, I see your hand's up.

Matt

Yeah, I know what it is. I don't play it, but my brother's a star on the Mohawk team. The game is lacrosse!

Sylvie

Oh, I saw a lacrosse game on TV once. It looked really fast and exciting!

Scene 2—Next day, on the playing field

Mr. Bailey
(blows his whistle) Okay, folks! I have someone to introduce to you. This is Matt's brother, Marcel. He's going to tell you all about lacrosse.

Marcel
Hi! So, you want to learn the game. I'll tell you about men's field lacrosse. Let's start by looking at the equipment. See this long stick with the basket thing on the end? Any guesses what it's for?

René
I guess you catch the ball with it.

Marcel
That's right, and throw the ball, too. As you know, you can't touch the ball with your hands. Matt, tell them about the ball.

Matt
Okay. It's very smooth and made of hard rubber. It's just a little smaller than a tennis ball.

Sylvie
And look at all the safety equipment—helmet, thick gloves, lots of pads. Do you really need all this when the ball's so small?

Marcel
Yes—both the ball and the stick can give you quite a whack. The protection is for heads, hands, shoulders, and arms.

Mr. Bailey

Sorry, people. Time's up for today. But Marcel will be back two days from now to show us how a game is played.

Scene 3—Two days later, on the playing field

René

Let's play a game, Marcel! It's no fun just looking at equipment.

Marcel

Patience, René. There are still a few things I need to show you. First of all, a lacrosse field is about 100 m long, and there's a net at either end. Any ideas how you score a point?

Monique

I bet you toss the ball into the net with your stick.

Marcel

You're right! Now, here's how the teams operate. There's a goalie, just like in hockey. There are three attackers, three mid-fielders, and three defenders.

René

I want to be an attacker!

Marcel

You're keen! I'd suggest playing mid-field. Those guys have to cover the entire field, playing both offence and defence. Okay, ready for some skills and drills?

Monique

Oh sure, I guess so. Seems like you always have to practise before you can play a sport properly.

Marcel

It's true. All right, the first skill is scooping. If you drop the ball onto the ground, you need to be able to scoop it up again. Scooping's important for the face-off, too.

René

That sounds like fun. What's the next skill?

Marcel

It's called cradling. Once you have the ball in the basket of your stick, you have to keep it there. You need to be able to run, turn, and stop without dropping it.

Monique

What about scoring goals?

Marcel

Okay, slow down. To score, a player needs to shoot the ball from a good position near the goal. The whole team helps. That's why catching and passing are the important skills.

Mr. Bailey

We're going to practise scooping, cradling, passing, catching, and shooting for the next couple of weeks. Then Marcel is going to take us on a special trip to the Mohawk reserve. That's where you'll get your chance to play in a real game!

Scene 4—At the Mohawk reserve

Marcel

Welcome to the reserve, everybody! Follow us. Matt's going to explain how our father makes traditional lacrosse sticks.

Matt

(arriving at his father's workshop) Well, my father is steaming this plank of wood so that he can bend the basket end into shape. Then he'll use wires to hold the shape till it dries. That takes at least six months!

Marcel

You know, long ago we Mohawks played lacrosse a lot. It kept the men strong and fit for hunting. We even played lacrosse to settle disagreements.

Matt

But we didn't call our game "lacrosse" back then. That's the name the French settlers gave it. Some people still call the stick a "crosse."

Marcel

That's right. Later, a man from Montreal, William George Beers, saw the game being played right here and fell for it. He helped make lacrosse popular all around the world.

Mr. Bailey

Very interesting. Now we'd better hustle over to the lacrosse field. There's a team out there just waiting for you guys to join them!

Scene 5—At the lacrosse game

Sylvie

Wow! I can't wait to play. Let's suit up and get onto the field!

René

Finally, our first real game! Good thing all the other team members know what they're doing.

Matt

Watch the face-off, guys. Hey! Our team got the ball first. Get ready for a pass.

Monique

I can't believe it! I caught the pass! What should I do now?

Sylvie

Run with it, Monique! Maybe you can shoot for a goal!

René

Pass it over here, Monique. I'm right near the net.

Matt

Great pass, Monique! Oops, René fell and dropped the ball. I'll try to scoop it up. Got it! *(Matt shoots the ball toward the net.)*

Sylvie
Yeah! Matt scored!

Marcel
Okay, team. That's the end of the first half. Come over here for some coaching tips.

René
What a team—the guys we're playing with can really move! And we four are doing well for the first time out! We might even help the team win!

Marcel
It's thanks to all those drills you've been doing for the last couple of weeks. Now, in the second half, I want you to keep the ball away from the other team and pass, pass, pass!

Mr. Bailey
Thanks, Marcel. I know René, Matt, Sylvie, and Monique will do their best. Everyone's falling for lacrosse! Three cheers for the best coach ever!

René, Matt, Sylvie, and Monique
Yeah, Marcel!

Comparison Chart

A comparison chart helps you see what is the same and what is different about things. You can use a comparison chart to organize information about a topic.

Sports Old and New

Lacrosse is Canada's oldest national sport. It has been played by Aboriginal peoples for centuries. Now thousands of Canadians enjoy this fast-paced, competitive sport.

Canadians have also started playing a new game—Ultimate Frisbee. This game was created in the 1960s by American high-school students. Ultimate Frisbee is also a fast-paced, competitive sport.

Look at the chart to see how these two sports compare.

LACROSSE AND ULTIMATE FRISBEE

Game	Lacrosse	Ultimate Frisbee
Description	• team sport • contact allowed • players run with the ball • to score a point, a player shoots the ball into the opponent's net • judged by referees	• team sport • no contact allowed • players are not allowed to run with the disc • to score a point, a player catches the disc in the opponent's **end zone** • judged by the players themselves
Equipment	• ball and lacrosse stick • triangle-shaped goal • shoes with cleats • protective pads and helmet	• Frisbee or disc • plastic cones to mark the playing field and end zones • shoes with cleats • no pads or helmet
Key skills	• throwing • catching • running • cradling and scooping	• throwing • catching • running
Playing area	• a field or hockey rink area	• a field, hockey rink area, or gymnasium
Teams	• 6 to 12 players on each team • players include **attackers**, **defenders**, mid-fielders, and a goalie	• 7 players on each team • all players act as throwers, receivers, and defenders; there is no goalie

Do a Radio Commercial

A key idea in Ultimate Frisbee is the "Spirit of the Game"—the idea that players must respect their opponents. Use the Internet to find out more, and tell what you learn in a 30-second radio commercial.

1. Use these key words to begin your search:

   ultimate   Frisbee

2. Learn about the game's rules and the "Spirit of the Game."

3. With a partner, write a script for a radio commercial promoting Ultimate Frisbee.

4. Tape-record your commercial, and play it for your classmates.

Experiment with Throwing

Throwing is a big part of many sports. With a partner, experiment with the equipment that players throw.

1. Collect a Frisbee and at least three different types of sports balls, such as a baseball or football.

2. Create a chart like this one.

Piece of equipment	Frisbee	basketball	___ ball	___ ball	___ ball
Size					
Weight					
Distance thrown					

3. Fill in the chart for each piece of equipment. For the row "Distance thrown," throw the equipment and measure the distance it travels.

4. Summarize what you learned in a paragraph.